ERRORS OF THE SPIRIT

Also by Joolz

POETRY

Mad, Bad and Dangerous to Know
(Virgin Books 1986)

Emotional Terrorism
(Bloodaxe Books 1990)

The Pride of Lions
(Bloodaxe Books 1994)

FICTION

Stone Baby
(HarperCollins 2000)

Errors of the Spirit

JOOLZ

FLAMBARD

ACKNOWLEDGEMENTS

I would like to thank Steve Pottinger for his unfailing support
and kindness; Margaret and Peter of Flambard for their calm
and good humour; and Mark Radcliffe for boldly and
poetically going where no DJ has gone before.
Also my thanks to the many people from all over the world
who wrote and e-mailed me with their support for this book.
Thank you Finn Mac Cool and Screamer –
and, of course, as ever, my thanks and respect to the Goddess.

JOOLZ

Flambard wishes to thank Northern Arts for its financial support.

First published in England in 2000 by Flambard
Stable Cottage, East Fourstones, Hexham NE47 5DX

Typeset by Barbara Sumner
Cover design by Gainford Design Associates
Printed in England by Cromwell Press, Trowbridge, Wiltshire.

A CIP catalogue record for this book
is available from the British Library

ISBN 1 873226 37 3

Contents

For Justin Sullivan and Warren Hogg

Idem velle atque idem nolle, ea demum firma amicitia est.

SALLUST

Under the Bridge

There's a café in the Arndale Centre – next to where the escalators crawl up and down loaded with fuzzy children and women drooping with Argos bags. It's the sort of open-plan, designer-twiddly, stale-scone and sour-coffee type of café that you end up in, rather than seek out. Anyway, for some reason they built a couple of fake gazebos in it, each with two tables. They look rather like little stages and that's where the girls sit.

Now, a number of interesting things have happened in this café, like, for example, why they don't have proper spoons anymore, and the time a bloke threatened to come back with a shooter and do the manageress on account of her asking him not to smoke in the non-smoking area, and – loads of stuff, really. I sit and watch in there – I watch and the people I see, see me watching but they don't care – or at least, they haven't yet.

So, this afternoon, the left-hand gazebo was fully occupied by a gang of girls all around seventeen or so, all about as loud as girls can be, which as you know is pretty damn loud, and you could see the shoppers were scared by this noise and the swearing, which was being laid on thick for the public benefit. The girls were all races and all combinations of races possible, Bradford pick'n'mix. What they had in common was their hair, which was worn in a high topknot, and their lipstick, which was the colour of dead red roses. The blunt muzzles of their faces pushed forward from the sticky wads of that processed hair like hunting hounds on the scent; their fingers were amber with nicotine, the nails spattered with plum varnish. They were singing 'Under the Bridge' – *take me to the place I love, take me all the way* – in close harmony. Fallen angels sing that way, coarse and soulful. But it frustrated them that they didn't know all the words so they fell to quartering the gazebo and abusing any lads who went past.

The shoppers' disapproval of all this behaviour was indicated by pursed lips, bridling and eyes cast heavenwards – but it was silent. No one would chance the girls, no one – me included – would mess with them. A palpable violence steamed off them, a kind of heated fury that lit their beautiful, gleaming eyes and set their necks stiff with tension. They weren't the limp, chattering, flip-bright, eighteen-year-old girls of the University, say, with their soft little paws full of a neat future and the safety net of home, class and money. The gazebo girls were raw with the grinding clamp of their tomorrows; fighting a last, snapping rearguard action against the dead certainty of their fate. They don't look up with their faces full of starlight, full of clarity and hope; they bite and scratch and kick out with their big old shoes at the leash that tightens daily.

The shoppers, the security guards and the rest in that cruddy, buy-cheap-and-sell-dear excuse for a café looked at the girls and only saw common little bitches acting up. Which they were – but then again, can you think of a real good reason – like, a really, really *good* reason why they shouldn't? Nah, neither can I.

The Seeker

No terrible counterpoint to the dead heat raging,
all the sorrow of the world's heart grieving;
what we hear in the salt sea crashing
is an old, abandoned mother sobbing
for her children's desolation.
Look at them running through the dank city
baying for blood and reparation;
the oldest consolation of revenge and desecration.

Sit still, and hold your breath ...
you are clean and neat,
they tell me your family has money.
Don't look round – don't move, it's not wise.
I believe you can hear it, can't you?
That sound – rising and falling,
that cruel, rending sound like
metal tearing, children breaking.
Something without a name, from the spirit.
Sit still, please – it may pass us by.

It's a blind thing, this monster
swinging its great head to and fro, seeking;
like a bull, heavy, slabbed with muscle,
only not – if you look closely, not at all.

The sun rises again, again, again;
and if I were you, I'd be very still,
really – very, very still.

A Terrible Beauty

She had the bloom of a peach on her – her skin velvety and matte, her lips gleaming with lipstick, the perfect Cupid's Bow, the Paris Pout. She was clever with make-up, using it to emphasise her resemblance to that other luscious beauty, Marilyn Monroe. That's what she was, a sort of Punk Marilyn – a composition of curves in pink and bleach blonde. Men always whistled, boys always shouted, girls always bitched and prattled, saying she was fat, she was common, she was a slut. She was, too – but when she swayed into the pub, a black lace choker at her creamy, rounded throat, her pale hair swept up and her tight black dress covering everything and showing it all, you forgave the guttural voice and the tumble of vulgarities. She was perfect, *perfect* – like a goddess or a pin-up painted on the nose of a bomber.

I was her mate for a while. I'd say 'friend' but she didn't really have friends – now I think she didn't know how. It was a pattern. At first she'd take up with you, hang on your arm screaming and giggling like a drunken princess, the harsh sweet cheapness of her perfume mixing with the smell of Pernod and Black – not unpleasant, but strong. That phase would go on for a few weeks. She'd be round your house in the afternoons (we were all on the dole) playing at hairdressers, doing your face, trying on all your clothes. Then you'd be out one evening and she'd turn on you when she'd had a few and create a huge scene. You'd protect her, take her home, look after her – how could you not? She was *so* sorry afterwards, so tearful and confiding. You'd let it pass because what she told you in her little-girl voice about her home life made you want to make it all better, made you understand why she did the things she did.

But the scenes would become a regular thing. So would the nasty tales she spread about you and the nicking money from your purse. When it got to fighting and she clawed your face with her immaculate long nails – well, things drifted. Loyalty was one thing, but … You remembered stories of her cruelty to her pet kitten; the drugs, the drink, the endless scandals. Later, rumours of sado-masochism – the strange dead look in her eyes sometimes and her pleasure in inflicting pain. *What a mess*, you thought; *poor thing,* you thought, *and so beautiful, too; such a terrible shame* – as if her beauty should have made her good. Like all the others she put through these tests, you failed because you couldn't win. You couldn't. She didn't want you to.

Years passed. I heard she went to Italy, what a sensation she must have made there, I thought, with those looks – *bella, bellissima.* She came home with a baby – and a monkey on her back. At last she'd discovered heroin. Social workers took the child away – just as well, really, because there was some tale about her trying to sell it. She was never interested in it anyhow, except it got her the sympathy vote sometimes, at the dole office. She was still exquisite, it seemed – thinner, all cheekbones and luminous eyes. She whored of course, what else? She could hardly write her own name and she had a lot of money to find.

A mutual acquaintance looked after her when she was committed for detox and for, well, 'personality disorders'. She was hell to nurse, always backsliding, having sex with the male – and female – patients. Getting caught, of course, and just laughing, laughing that loud, throaty giggle. My friend said her case file was a nightmare, a pure horror story of abuse and self-destruction. She would shake her head and sigh; *it's no wonder she's like she is, it's amazing she's still alive – and so pretty! Still gorgeous, it's weird …*

She died, eventually, in Manchester, of an overdose. I think she finally achieved her ambition. No doubt she made a beautiful corpse. In life, the beauty she was born with – had never asked for – cost her everything. Childhood, innocence, protection of family, everything. Like the legendary woman she so resembled, she was, apparently, too much of a temptation for any man to resist. Even her father and uncles – *especially* them. I forget how long Marilyn held out for – Samantha got to twenty-six. I'm amazed she got that far.

Goodnight, sweetheart – goodnight.

The Sea (Polzeath)

The day closes with a seam of fire edging the sky into the sea;
the headland flings its giant arm around the bay and a sparkle of
      lights
prickles through the darkness on the hills.

Up to my chest in the inky sea, the swell lifts and falls lazily like
      mercury;
it has that liquid, metallic heaviness, the foam
spreading like bridal lace and the rack of stars above me.

Sometimes, twitching in her ancient, giant sleep, the sea
will fling you off and under, rolling you in brine, giving you
      water
to breathe, returning you in your dying to your beginnings;
a little fish, blind and helpless.

My grandmother said you must never swim out to sea
along the silver path the moon lays in the water,
because you'll get stuck in it and never be able to turn back.

She was right.

Baby

He holds the baby to his chest like a totem;
a lucky charm that will save him from the shadows.
It feels to him as if its helplessness will
give him power into the future,
that now he is real – he is *real* and no one
will forget he lived while this unformed
image of himself lives and moves within the world.
He feels furious with love and triumph,
he feels like God in this creation;
he feels … a terrible fear that he won't be
able to protect this best and sweetest part of him
against the life he's known too well.

And his crooked, calloused finger strokes the
child's face in a promise of defence he knows he can't fulfil.

Joey and the Gypsy King

In the end, all the talking came to nothing.

Joey knew, without Uncle Benny even saying anything, that he had to fight the Gypsy King. That was his job – that was his life. The family expected him to do his duty. He was not ashamed, neither was he afraid. The Gypsies had overstepped the mark, tried to take what wasn't theirs. They were foolish not to back off – so now, Joey would make things even again.

In business, negotiation was always best; but the Gypsies were angry and wouldn't hear reason. They'd been greedy and got caught cheating. This alone was enough to make them furious, but add to that the little matter of one of their women running off with Joey's cousin Rafe, well … This was the only way. Their King against Joey. It was fair, in his opinion.

He went to the site in the afternoon, to look at the ground picked for the fight. The screaming racket of the rock music was already beginning, though the Festival wasn't due to start until the next day. The area was dotted with scruffy fans, doped and foolish – at least in Joey's eyes. He and they were of the same age, on the whole. But Joey's twenty-five years had been spent in a way these people could never understand. He sighed. Had he been missing anything? No – he thought not. He was a man, with responsibilities, with a life. This lot, they wanted to stay kids forever – he could have no respect for them.

The concessions – the stalls – food, drink, and the cheap, ethnic trash the festivalgoers loved so much, traditionally brought the family a great deal of money in site fees and security work. The Gypsies knew this, but had still tried to take over. Standing with his suit jacket draped over one shoulder, Joey breathed in the stink of burnt fat and nameless meat; sniffing the acrid air already thick with the reek of dust, sewage and a faint, dark whiff of patchouli oil. He shook his head, bewildered at the idea anyone would pay a small fortune to live like *this* for three days.

He went back to his car, where Gennaro and Eddy were waiting. He drank a little mineral water and took off his sunglasses, throwing them into the front seat of the Jaguar. Then he removed all his jewellery except for his crucifix, giving the heavy gold to Gen to hold for him, along with his jacket and tie. He took off his shirt and stood waiting in his white vest and black suit trousers. The brothers were silent, they knew not to disturb him when he was preparing himself.

And the Gypsy King came, with his men all dressed in their best – waiting to see their leader beat this boy bloody. The King was a thick-set man in his early forties, strong and hard. His curling black hair gleamed with oil. He smiled at Joey, gold glinting in his mouth, and walked to the centre of the space. He called out to Joey to come and fight, then said something in his own language which made his men laugh.

Joey looked at the sky, squinting slightly. Then he crossed himself and walked to face the King. There was a moment like the surface tension of water before Joey took the King down in a long series of blows that broke bone, fractured cartilage and pooled blood, red and precious, on the dusty dirt floor.

It was over quickly. Though the King was used to the brutality of such encounters, he was older, slower, than Joey, who had trained all his life for this sort of thing. The King knelt on the dirt, gasping; pain eating his guts and his lungs heaving for air through his broken face.

Joey took the towel Eddy handed him and wiped his hands and face. Then he drank some more water. He looked at the King as his men took him away – and felt nothing. The King had fought well, but really it had been no contest. He'd been past his prime. Gennaro, smiling as he always did, gave Joey back his things and helped him on with his jacket.

The sun was beginning to set. Tomorrow the name bands would play and the hordes of punters flood happily into the site. Again Joey sighed. He couldn't comprehend their ignorance. He'd heard somewhere, ignorance was bliss. *What was knowledge then?* he thought; and getting into the car with the brothers, drove away.

15

The Story

Right – so, I went to this party a while since – not a very common occurrence for me as I don't socialise much. But there I was, and it was OK – as these things go. Not exactly a wild, swinging affair, just lots of people all trying to be grown-up and that sort of party wine that tastes of petrol.

After a while, I found myself sitting at a table chatting with a group of folks I didn't really know, about nothing much of consequence, and wishing it was a bit later so I could slope off home unnoticed to a crap late-night film on Channel Five and a cup of tea. To be honest, now, I can't even remember what it was I'd said – some anecdote or other – what was it about? No – no, I don't recall.

But whatever it was, the lad across the table from me cut in and said, in a wire-tight voice that was still burred with the long vowels and choppy sentences of the country, that it reminded him of something that happened to him as a child. I looked at him close, for the first time, and noticed the things I'd missed before, when he'd seemed just another croppy-headed blond kid trying to be arty whose girlfriend fussed over him a fraction too much for someone of that age.

He was definitely country, with the blunt face and stain of suntan that comes from generations of people who squint at the sky in a dull terror and study weather reports like they were the Bible. His eyes were dark, deep-set and his complexion had a damp, slightly slipped look that made him seem out of focus. I said – *Oh, right?* Like – OK, tell me, then.

The others chattered across us for a bit, like city people do who are used to talking and not hearing. But they stopped after a while as the lad told the tale of a vile and unpardonable act of sadism that had been done to him and his friend, in the name of rustic amusement, when they were little. It was to do with the torturing of animals for sport and other things that go on in the hidden places tourists and us urban types never see on our day trips and our rented cottage holidays. It was to do with blood and mutilation, and it was one of the more horrible confessions I have received in a long, long life of hearing things I wish I hadn't. I won't repeat it.

Some people got up and left the table – one man was retching and not because of the cheap wine. The others busied themselves forgetting as fast as they could until it was just the boy, and me, and the rotting web of that story binding him to his past and me to him, as he repeated the thing that had held him in its sticky threads since he'd seen it and heard the sounds he could never forget. He didn't blink, nor did he raise his voice, and he spoke like a sinner who hopes that in the repetition of the Word lies salvation – that if he told the tale often enough it would fade – become an old, feeble thing, worn out and powerless.

Then there was a moment – a long, silent moment – full of nothing sayable, broken only by his little girlfriend, who hustled him away quickly while the others began a brisk conversation about mortgages.

I left shortly afterwards and watched that silly film, and drank my tea and wished I'd stayed at home; wished I'd sat at another table; wished I didn't have that story in my head like a putrid, squat *thing* I can't be rid of. And I only had it second-hand. That boy – he has to carry it like a disease, a tumour sitting in his heart for the rest of his days. And no sun will shine for him that isn't tainted by it, and no moon will rise that doesn't carry with it the threat of dreams.

Otter

for Jack

The old dog otter sat by the edge of his little pool,
in his little enclosure, and ignored the people
twittering and cooing behind the fence.
The keeper brought him some dead fish
and threw them into his pool, so he would swim down
and let the people watch him though the glass-sided viewing tank;
he was never out of their sight.
But though he dived for the food into the dark water
he didn't eat it, the swimming was enough,
and he himself – melancholy, graceful, sheathed in silver air
      bubbles –
was more beautiful than the day.

I asked the keeper why, out of all the other otters,
this one was alone. He told me that there had been a mate,
but she had become ill and died at the Vet's.

He said, 'You have to be careful when that happens, you see,
you've got to take the body back to the pen
and leave it there, so the living otter
will find its dead companion.
See, when they do, they try to sit the body up,
they try to open its eyes, to move its limbs around.
They cry over it, you know, hour after hour,
those little mewling voices calling and calling …
Well, they go on like this for about a week,
and then they cover the body up with grass and leave it.
So then you know you can take it away.
You've got to do all this, right, or else they go crazy
and hurt themselves searching for the lost one.
They have to bury their dead, you see,
they have to go through it all, say their goodbyes,
they have to bury their dead.'

Snapshot

I only met him once, though I had heard the stories of his short life; how he had, after a quarrel with another boy, put a stolen shotgun up against the lad's temple and calmly threatened to splatter his brains all over the wall. He was about fourteen then, or maybe less. It seemed he burned with a still white flame of madness that was not wild or hot, in the way of youth, but steady and inexorable. He worked on the London building sites where his strength came in useful, labouring long hours like a machine, unless someone annoyed him.

He would have been sixteen when I came across him, in a pub on a decaying estate. It was sunny outside and the stained-glass window washed his pale, blocky face with ruby and sapphire. He was very quiet. I think it was a struggle for him to speak. In the shifting colours his fathomless eyes were like black jelly, expressionless and fixed … In his way, he was polite, though without doing anything. You could see his presence made the other men uncomfortable. The bloody shadows of the glass shifted over him as he got up to leave, and I noticed, for some reason, despite the unspeakable alienness of him, his mouth was the unformed soft mouth of a child, and I remembered what one of the others had told me he'd said after the shotgun thing:

I don't need friends, I've got an army in my head …

Sometimes I think of that and wonder what happened to him – but I doubt I'll ever find out. The world swallows the likes of him like the old god eats his children.

Shark

She never knew why he picked her – there were two other girls around, both young, both dressed in the baby-doll fashions of the summer, just like her. Maybe there was something in the way *she* looked that reminded him of someone else; another time, another girl. Maybe it was just random. Still, she was well pleased when the smart black Porsche pulled up, and she ran to the side window smiling and smiling. They liked it if you smiled, talked babyish, that sort of thing, and she was desperate that night – they all were, the girls. It had been very quiet – too quiet. Their boyfriends would not be best pleased with the takings and one of the other girls, Emma, and herself were beginning to feel a bit poorly. They did have some blow with them but it was hardly the same as what they really needed.

The punter was a well-dressed, older bloke. The car smelt of expensive aftershave. They agreed a price for oral, then she got in and they drove off. The other girls tried to take the number of the car down, for safety's sake, but their biro didn't work – then two cars turned up virtually together and that was that.

She liked riding in the beautiful car; he put some classical music on low, then asked her name in a polite way and she told him – Caz, short for Caroline. He smiled and asked her age; when she told him she was just turned fourteen, he smiled again. She noticed the seats were covered in thin plastic sheeting and asked him why, for something to say. *It had just returned from the valeting company*, he said, *and oh – here we are, the multi-storey, will this do? Oh yes,* she said, *go to the top floor, it's nice and quiet.*

As they drove round and up, she thought how one day she'd have a smart car, smart clothes, jewellery, loads of cash. How she'd make it up with Mum, make her understand she hadn't been lying about what Dad had done, and they'd have a good cry together and everything would be OK again. Maybe this fella'd take a fancy to her and be a regular like some of the others had – maybe even set her up in her own little place. She could have smashing things then, she could …

He started hitting her without speaking. She was so shocked she didn't scream. He broke her nose first, then her jaw and he didn't stop beating on her until he came, which took quite a long time. Towards the end he was hissing things at her but she couldn't take it in. Oddly enough she thought – *oh, that's what the plastic sheeting's for*. Then he opened the door and threw her onto the oily concrete, and she passed out as he drove off.

Emma came to visit her at the Infirmary, but Caz couldn't speak or anything and Emm got dead upset at the state of her. The Police asked Emm a lot of questions but it was no good, she hadn't really seen anything – just a posh sort of car, darkish, never saw the driver. They shook their heads, the coppers, and Emm knew nothing would come of it except the lasses would all be chased around by social workers for a bit and have to go back to the Care Home. One of the coppers was a woman and Emm thought she'd be sympathetic, but she said, *What d'you lot expect? Look, stay in the Home where you're put, it's for your own good.* Emm just nodded, but it's like they always said – why stay in there and have to do blowjobs for free when you can get good money for it outside?

She stopped a nurse who looked kind. *Excuse me*, she said, *but my friend Caz – Caroline I mean – will she, like, be alright? See, I can't come visit again, my boyfriend, he don't like it, so – will she, d'you think, be alright, like? What does Doctor say? Will she be alright – you know – will she?*

Grendel

This is not *me* speaking, but of course my ghost.
There, it shocks you doesn't it? Oh, not that I'm *dead*,
which of course you already knew – but that I can
speak as well, as *coherently* as you.
Really, you expected some slavering, grunting beast,
something from the sluggish pit of a black past,
and what do you get – an educated monster,
a literate whelp of Hell. Well, I can't help that.
It's my fate to be misunderstood.
If I am an ogre, you made me so,
willing as you are to believe the pathetic bundle of lies
that idiot monk scratched and blotted laboriously
by guttering rushlight all that time ago.
My, how the ages pass – flickering, brief as moth wings
while I hang here, remembering.

I am Grendel, last of the Children of Cain,
Fen-Lord, Master of the Tarns, Prince of the Marches.
I am a legend, yet a legend with no voice –
just a spectre to frighten children with,
and no one knows the truth of my life but me …
Of course, everyone knows the saga – how mighty Beowulf
(that famous warrior, so in love with death he spasmed
in its chilly embrace like a spring-sick boy)
fought the hideous, lumbering giant, Grendel,
ripped the Creature's arm from its socket with his bare hands
then chased the howling brute through the grim night to
finish off the Beast's disgusting mother in the peat-dark
water of their outcast lair. And all in glorious
defence of Hrothgar's beloved Heorot, Home of Heroes, Hall of
     Victory,
the world's most *beautiful* building.

Here I float, a seed of consciousness in this
great unbounded limbo and I have no rest.
Heorot, that *vanity*, that gaudy cavern, haven

to those beer-swilling idiots clanking and boasting
in the gore-crusted link-mail of their bloody persecutions.
There's always another side to things, you know.
Just think a little – just consider that this renowned story,
so butchered by that sapless scrivener of the White Christ,
could be so much propaganda, a farrago of fanaticism.
The truth was somewhat different. It was like this.

As a child, I watched Heorot being built – we all did.
If the Danes knew we were there, spying,
they didn't give a sign of it – they just hauled the timber
and up it grew – the hateful symbol of our oppressors.
It was hardest for me, though. Somehow I was
fascinated by it, it drew me night and day.
I would lie in the shade of the scrub for hours, watching.
Then, in the comforting dark, I would prowl
around the walls, snuffing up their smells,
scenting the acrid stink of Danish sweat, piss and puke.
There were chinks in the walls, too – not so well made
as they say, that place – and I would put my eye to them and peer
into the golden fire of it; hot with torches and
wick with the flicker of the huge hearth.
I would listen to their fat, stupid, *meaty* row and be
filled with so much rage and envy I'd roll on the filthy
ground silently wailing to Our Lady the Moon
to bring it all crashing down around their pig-thick skulls.
Then I would slink off home to Mother, crying.
This went on for years as our numbers dwindled
and our settlements were destroyed by those brave, brave
warriors – ever quick to stick our children on their spears
and spill our women's guts. All that *cutting*, all that blood.

In the end, they had massacred us. Genocide – hah!
They wanted no traces of the Old Ones left
in their bright new world. We were anathema.
They called us monsters, unnatural, evil progeny of the dark.
They counted it a sport to slaughter us. We were *dead*.
So, it was a few scattered remnants and Mother
and me in the last tarn-cave, together.

What can I tell you about Mother?
Of course, she was Mother of us All,
not just my own mother – I was nobility, if you like.
Hence my educated tongue and *charming* speech.
That's why we survived – we were protected by the Clans.
If Mother died, it was finished – all the knowledge,
the Lists of Names, the Cures and Poisons,
the Songs and Stories and the Magic,
it was all in her head – without her, we were nothing.
And naturally she was a great warrior.
I was good, though I say so myself – but she was better.
Perhaps we *were* too close, too … intimate,
but it was the Old Way. To us, it was natural.
The Christians with their mewling, dirty minds
hadn't crept into the land then.
Ah, Mother … She was beautiful, you know – truly.
Brown and strong, with bird-bright eyes full of understanding.
She tried to save me from my rage, my twisting bitterness,
she tried to kiss away the fury, to make me accept
what couldn't be changed. In her arms I felt,
if not better, then at least release in the little death …
But it was no use, she couldn't save me
or (oh, my dark love) I her.

Then at last, she told me the Secret.
I finally understood why Heorot had drawn me so,
and what my heritage was.
And I knew what I had to do.
I must kill them all, consume their spirits through their flesh
and avenge my people.
I let the Dead take my hands and lead me to the slaughter,
screaming with the savage joy of it as the fit rode me.
I went among those cowards, drunk and fat with lies as they
        were,
like a storm of fire, sparing none, eating their
hot and smoking hearts until I was sickened with the taste
and drenched in the crimson of their veins.
And the Dead laughed inside my head to see the vengeance
I took, night after night, a veritable Demon,
the very Child of Cain, as the Christians would have it.

I was without mercy and without fear.
I was unstoppable. And because the Danes were in terror,
they whispered of my monstrosity, malign,
pitiless and bestial; they made me – *inhuman*.

Then Beowulf came – Hrothgar called him from
his own lands, subtly, with a sigh, a whisper
a well-placed word in a traveller's ear.
He knew the Geat would come, but since he had
never actually *asked*, it would seem Beowulf came of his own
      accord,
and Hrothgar could play the innocent victim, rescued
by the great Hero from persecution by the unspeakable Fiend.
I believe his wife suggested that … or was it Unferth,
that greasy serpent, Hrothgar's favourite sycophant?
Many nights I had searched amongst the sleeping gluttons
for *that* devil's get, Unferth, but the craven
always hid himself too well … ah, lost opportunities …
Beowulf, Beowulf – with his savage face and his courtesy …
From the first, I knew we had a lot in common – he was dark,
      you know.
That's why the Danes weren't *comfortable* with him,
even though they knew how to use his mania
to serve themselves. In his eyes burnt the same
death-wish that lit mine – I think we could have
been, not *friends*, but something, something . . .
It made me loathe the Danes still more,
watching them getting a good man to do their dirty work for
      them.
So, in the end, we fought, my Beowulf and I,
perfectly matched – it was like a dance of love.
I wanted to kiss him, to embrace him as a brother.
It distracted me and in a second (so quick he was, so clever)
he cut my arm from my body with one shining
slice of his iron knife. He didn't *tear* it off
as that fool said – he was a *man*, not a god.
Then I felt the poison of the sky-metal in me like acid
and my life pumping out on Hrothgar's floor,
so with a last curse, I fled; leaving a gore-trail
back to the caves – and Mother.

She held me, dying, drenched in my blood.
Her black hair was dappled with it as if she'd braided
hawthorn berries in its gleaming length.
I remember that – she looked so – *unearthly* …
I made her swear to eat my heart, according to
the custom, so she would be strong and full of power
when they came for her, as we both knew they would.
And then … Beowulf thrust glittering in from the night,
screaming, possessed by his berserker's rage,
and I, helpless, my life pooling red
onto the cavern floor, watched the last Great Mother
slaughtered by the Wyrd of my race, the battle-maddened
      Beowulf,
cat's-paw of the Betrayer, Hrothgar, our doom-bringer.
I heard my mother's dying screams as she struggled
to destroy the man who had murdered her only child.
The Son of the Mother – sacred, dedicated to the Land
and born out of the Darkness by a Mother trance-bound in the
Old Mysteries, fathered by the Earth-King
in a ritual older than the stars.

Do you understand now?
Mother was my mother and my father was
Hrothgar, Earth-King, Lord of the Danes.

That's why I hated him so, I was his Dark Son,
the Child of the Great Mating – the offspring of a pact
between his race and mine, between the Old Ways
and the New – meant to bind us, if not together,
then at least in mutual respect.

Oh, Hrothgar, my unnatural father,
did you never think of me as you drank yourself
insensible every night and ploughed your fat wife's furrow
to the music of your snoring thanes?

Did you never think how *I* felt, peering into
your lighted Hall, built with the gold you stole
from the Barrows of my ancestors?
Did you hesitate at all in denying our Goddess

for your pathetic, squabbling Godlings?
And when the Christians came, creeping into the
hearts of the fearful with their sick theology,
did you hesitate for a second to be dowsed in the water
and profess the True Cross like a child greedy for love?

I saw it all. Death sent me spinning into nothingness,
into this cold, ancient darkness all alone,
a *phantom* – powerless to do anything but watch.
I saw the years pass and my beautiful Beowulf kill himself
in that last, impure battle; tired of life, tired of
heroism and the burdens of his honour and his violence …
I howled for him, here in my eternal night –
but he could not hear me …
I am just a spark, a shiver that runs over your skin,
a whisper in your mind as you hover on the brink of sleep …
I am Grendel – mightiest of Monsters.
Loneliest of all the sad sons of Time,
and this is *my* saga, *my* story never before told.
Still shocked? Well, well, never mind.
The little flame of your living flickers lower with every sunset
and you'll join me soon enough, soon enough …

Spoons

If you look down on the Gazebo Café in the Arndale Centre from the crawling escalator, it looks like some fool just chucked a load of cheap garden furniture in the kind of cross-roads between the posh dress shop and Smith's. The higher the wheezing, cronky metal stairs climb, the tattier the café becomes. It just doesn't look permanent; solid. But, despite appearances, it's been there for years, dishing up its evil, undrinkable coffee, leathery baked potatoes and polystyrene cakes in varying shades of beige.

When they first set it up, it was meant to be a bit smart, a bit modern – in that erstaz, flimsy, corporate catering sort of way. But that was before the out-of-town retail malls really took off, when the Arndale was still the place to go and shop. Oh, at first, in the café's brief, shiny heyday, there were spoons – proper metal spoons – teaspoons, I mean. But like Shaz said to me – she was the manageress at the time, a nice woman, very bright, too bright for there, really – it wasn't to last. Slowly but surely all the spoons went missing. *Costs the company a bloody fortune,* Shaz used to say, dragging deeply on a Benson's as we sat in the smoking area and her light, careful eyes constantly scanned the café for trouble. *They won't hack it, anymore – this place is hanging on by a bloody thread – so I'm sorry, but from now on it's plastic stirrers. That'll piss the thieving little bastards off. You can't cook your gear on a plastic stirrer.*

Junkies were stealing the spoons, you see. Steal a spoon, nip down to the nice, big, clean toilet in the new Waterstone's and bob's yer uncle. Then Waterstone's got sick of fishing nodders out of their convenience and started making you put a pound deposit down for using the toilet, and the café got stirrers. I don't know what the junkies thought about all this – I never asked one – but it pissed me off. Same as it pisses me off being followed round Boots by some geek in a Security Operative's uniform because the junkies have shoplifted the place ragged trying to raise the price of their shot at Heaven.

So in the end, the city takes on the shape of the drug its citizens currently favour. Without anyone saying anything. Like a ghost image being pressed down on the blurry faces of the folk who circle and drone round the same, dying shops and the same crap caffs in town. And the other people, the people with cars and money, the ones who consider themselves decent and reasonable, go to the big malls and don't concern themselves – past the odd tut and head-shake – about the lives of the rest.

Sometimes in the newspapers or on television you see articles or programmes about young, beautiful, wealthy people from good homes who are found to be regular heroin users. Or you might read about the tremendous amount of skag or coke consumed by high-flying City traders, modern artists, or Members of Parliament. These things are reported as a tragedy – albeit a fashionable one – a waste of potential, or a fall from grace. The victims, distraught at being caught out in this way, are treated in private clinics, forgiven, interviewed by magazines, rehabilitated. They aren't prosecuted or detained at Her Majesty's Pleasure because it would interfere with their lifestyles and their careers.

In Bradford, lost in the North and scoured by the sharp, dusty wind that brings the scent of heather and emptiness from the surrounding moorlands, the prisons and scrubby, hopeless detox centres are full to overflowing with the wretched, the unrepentant, the savage and the lost.

And we don't have metal spoons anymore in the Gazebo Café.

Age

A while ago someone asked me
if I was less angry about things now I was old,
if I had *mellowed* with age.
They asked in that fake cheery way
people have if they're nervous,
and it was obvious that
they didn't really want to know the answer
in case I told the truth, or said something serious
that they wouldn't know how to cope with.

Normally, I try hard to be kind to people
who are frightened by little things, as I often am myself.
But that day – oh – I'd made the mistake of reading a newspaper,
or watching the television, or walking round town,
and some scorched images from another breathtaking
act of human savagery capered in my mind
like dead things dancing on the Ship of Fools.

Now, I realise patience is a virtue, but I don't have it.
So, I said that in my case at any rate
time just serves to concentrate anger and outrage
until it's thick and strong like boiled-down blood
and reeks like a dry iron pot heating on the stove.
Because you can try to stand still
and hope to be passed over in many ways,
and in many ways you will succeed;
but time proceeds against your will
and makes all the world's bare bones of cruelty rattle in your face.
So you can either stick your fingers
in your ears and chatter as loud as you can to try and
cover up that stony clatter; or understand that fury,
in its infinite variety, does not wither or grow stale
and time is the bolting horse we none of us can dismount.

Davey

See Davey standing in a sunny garden – an old snapshot
taken when he was nineteen: the light gilds his beautiful face
and thick shining hair, his strong white teeth bared in a smile.
You can see how tall and well-made he is, long-limbed
and classical, like a statue, like marble – all the light
comes to him hot as a lover, but it doesn't ignite those
pale, distant eyes; it doesn't really touch him.

Then, the coldness of him seemed only to prove
his bright intelligence, to put him apart from the
coarse, the mundane, the ill-made. The seeds of
what he would become were dormant in the dense
clotted flesh of his ruined heart. They waited
for time to let them root and bloom in him like a rank weed,
never spoiling his looks, just rotting him inside.

Davey walks like a hollow man with a demon wrapped
webby through his insides; it croaks through his
pretty mouth, slides tendrils of insanity across
the blue glass of his long eyes. What's left of who
he was is dwindling, dwindling down into the dirty depths –
just his pale shade of a face glimpsed, then gone,
his white hand grasping up – and missing.

Davey in the sun casts no shadow, now;
I lost him, I lost him, I lost my Davey boy.

The Good King

The full moon was caught in the branches of the tree I could see from the window as I lay tangled up in bed, and it seemed like sleeping was a waste of time. The air outside was razor sharp, the stars like the diamonds in my grandmother's eternity ring – pinpoints of dazzle dust – flickering, beckoning.

I sat up and pulled my tracksuit on. I knew my hair was stuck up all over like a child's and my eyes swollen, tired, but who was to see? The whole house would be sleeping – overtired, overfull of food and thickheaded from drink; the egg-nog, the wine and *how about a nice Bailey's? It's only Christmas once a year, we're only all together once a year, drink up, have another …*

I wanted some tea. I wanted to smell the sleeping house, to sit in the front room and look at the lights on the tree and the spilled-out board games, the books all new and box fresh, the scent of tangerines and pine. I wanted to sit there and be six again, so I didn't hear or understand the sniping and bitching, the undertones and grumbling – had they always gone on like this? Was it always this hard to make a conversation without upsetting someone? When did it all become small talk – or no talk at all?

I turned to open the kitchen door, and stopped. I heard a noise, faint but definite. I heard someone in the kitchen crying. I opened the door as quiet as I could and sitting at the table in the dark was my father, crying. The stifled sobs were tearing at him and I never realised before, you know, I never realised until then he'd gone so grey. The moonlight silvered him and I heard him cry like the child I'd wished I was.

Well, I suppose, if this had been a film, I'd have walked right up to him and we'd have had a good talk and got to know each other as adults – respect, pride and *I love you, Dad*. But it wasn't a film, it was my father – the Hero, the Untouchable, Alexander, Hercules, Jason of the Argonauts and Good King of us all, crying, head in arms, on the mess of the kitchen table, in the cold moonlight and the savage frost. So I turned silently and left. He never heard me. I turned and crept back upstairs to my old single bed in the room with the ballerina wallpaper and I cried too. Because there lay between us a gulf I couldn't cross, and I was sorrier for that than just about anything else in my life …

But that's how it was, that's just how it was.

Marriage

I think it came as a bit of a shock to some people when I got married. People actually said, 'Well, I never thought *you'd* get wed, I really didn't.'

I just smiled, because inwardly I agreed with them. But once started, the whole process was quite unstoppable, and from the moment my boyfriend shyly handed over the engagement ring, we were caught up in a round of dresses, cakes and diplomacy that was to me hysterical and absolutely unconnected to the pair of us. We knew our mothers were in a feeding frenzy of bridal magazines and hat shops, but it wasn't *us*, it wasn't *me*. I was nineteen, but I felt like a child with no will of my own anymore.

It didn't take long once the machinery had been set in motion. My parents were horrified by my marrying into the working-classes; his parents weren't happy he was marrying a girl they considered unstable and strange. They were both right, but no one could have kept us apart. Our opposing cultures attracted us to each other, and though we knew we'd had totally different lives, we thought it didn't matter. It did. We had nothing in common but love and a curious gentleness with each other as if we knew in our hearts it wouldn't last. On the great day, I wore white; he'd bought a suit from C&A. My mother's outfit cost as much as the rest of the wedding and my mother-in-law looked like she'd been resurrected from the recently deceased for the event. Our families did their best – despite their disapproval – but on the whole it was all faintly disappointing, like these occasions are. Not *awful*, just … not what you dream of.

The first time someone called me 'Mrs' I looked around for who it was they were talking to. We lived in our little flat like children playing house, which is what we were. I couldn't cook – he couldn't talk. We drank cheap sweet cider and rode motorcycles around aimlessly with the gang. *We* weren't going to be straight, *we* weren't going to have a boring, conventional life. We were free spirits. I believed him when he agreed with me. I was so young, how could I have known how much he would come to crave what he'd been raised to? He spent his time – when not at work – in the attic, building a beautiful new bike, which had to be dismantled to get it down two flights of stairs. I was so lonely I behaved as badly as I knew how. He let me, in his sweet, baffled way, because he was only a boy and didn't know what to do. I loved him like a brother and left him after four years, kissing his tear-wet face goodbye at the lawyer's while we held hands, knowing we had no future together but missing what we did have. I haven't seen him since.

Now, as I look back, it's like a dream of someone else's life. For a long while, I couldn't remember his face. But these days, for some reason, I remember as clear as day how mild and blue his eyes were. I wonder if he ever thinks of me – and if he does, what he recalls.

I wonder how you can lose someone so completely without them dying.

Valentine

She was an ordinary girl; very young.
Not pretty, not plain – pale, plump,
her round face still and fathomless.

At her age, love comes like a blow,
it strikes like a clenched fist
making you senseless – have you forgotten?

But he didn't notice her, as he laughed
with his friends, or danced, or tried
out the faces he would use when he was a man.

She dyed her hair black; it lay false
and glittering iridescent against her downy cheek.
She wore ruby-coloured lipstick – nothing worked.

So one night when the darkening sky
was like a bruise, she lit candles stolen from her mother,
cut a little heart out of pink cloth,

and wrote his name on it in blood.
She burnt incense, bound up dust from his footprint with herbs
and salt; with a rose, red and velvety as passion;

with the broken blade of a pocketknife;
with a lock of her starling hair;
with a wish written circular widdershins;

with the Ace of Spades; with a musky drop of perfume;
with a piece of crimson embroidery thread knotted six times
while she chanted the words of her favourite song.

Then, in the silver gaze of the full moon,
she burnt it all in the garden, while her family slept dreamlessly
and she wept bitterly for her desire.

An ordinary girl, very young –
but old enough to know that sometimes,
the wanting of a thing is better by far than the getting of it.

Dusty's Story

I once knew a boy called Dusty, and he told me this one night a long time ago:

It started when I were about six year old. I were called Michael then – I won't have anyone call me that now. It were my mother's brother, Uncle Don – man, she thought the world of him. He used to be a Country and Western fan, like, fancied himself as a bit of a Johnny Cash look-alike – he allus wore this big, flappy black coat over a black Western shirt and jeans, and he had black pointy cowboy boots with silver toecaps. He had an American car, too. I liked him, he allus brought me sweets and stuff and I used to draw pictures of his car and give them to him.

Anyhow, one afternoon in summer he come round and said would Ma mind if he took me for a drive, for company, like, and off we went. He were humming some Country tune all the time and he kept saying – *well, Mick-Mike-Michael* (which were his name for me) *just us two fellas out and about, eh? No women to boss us round – let's have some fun!* We went to Hooper Woods, parked the car and walked right in amongst the trees. It were dark and cool in there and the sunlight came down in patterns through the branches, full of glittering, floating bits – you know what I mean – and it looked like fairyland or something. *Well, Mick-Mike-Michael*, he said, *let's enjoy ourselves.* Then he did stuff to me I wouldn't do to a woman. It – hurt a lot and I cried, but he told me all men did this. It were private, for men only, and I weren't to talk about it ever – *ever.* Especially to my Ma, like, because it were so private. Every bloke went through it – it were what made you a real man. If I blabbed about it, my family would be disgusted with me for being a coward and showing them up, and they'd throw me out, and send me to the Kids' Home where bad lads went. He said he'd take care of me though, see me through it, because I were special to him – his special little friend, his Mick-Mike-Michael. Of course I believed him – he were my uncle. He were a grown-up. So I shut up and watched the light through the trees while he got on with it.

It went on till I got too old for him – around thirteen. He just dropped me like a hot brick. I suppose I weren't *special* anymore – it were some other poor little sod's turn. I'd like to say I hated him – I mean, I hate him *now*, more than anything, more than I can say – but then … I *ought* to have hated him … but it weren't that easy. When we weren't riding round in that bloody car he were brilliant. I sort of forgot the things he did and I loved him – I did, in't that sick? And of course all the family thought he were great, they were allus laughing and joking together, having outings, barbecues and stuff. Mum and Dad were allus going on about what a great bloke he were. I felt like it were *me* who'd done wrong – who were wrong for not feeling the same as everyone else about him. Later, when I were older and understood what he'd done, like, I wanted to tell, I did – but I just knew they wouldn't believe me, plain and simple. It made me wild. I felt like an animal, a *freak*. I got into all sorts of trouble – man, trouble just used to come to me like I were a magnet. Fighting, lying, stealing – anything, everything – but it were never enough, it never stopped me feeling so bad. The funny thing is, like, Ma used to cry and carry on about how evil I were and say, *why can't you be like Don? He used to take such an interest in you, you should have stuck to him, he's a good influence.* I used to laugh and laugh and she'd say, *oh, you're so cold and hard, you're no son of mine.* So I thought, OK then, have it your own way – and I legged it, never went back. What were the point? I got the name 'Dusty' out of a football comic and I made everyone call me that. Not Mick, or Mike, or Michael – not ever.

Look, I know I'm not right, I know it. I try to be normal, like proper lads – but it don't work, it don't. Like, I were with this girl the other night – we was in bed – and she kept saying, *ooh, Mike, Mike*, and I just got right up off her in the middle of everything – got dressed and left without saying a word. I know I shouldn't have, but it were like I couldn't stop myself. She carried on terrible, crying and shouting at me – still calling me Mike – and I thought, if I don't get out of here I'll … well, I don't know what I would have done. I suppose it were cruel of me – but I had told her, my name is *Dusty* – nothing else. But, like, she thought nicknames were common, so in a way, it were her own fault really.

He robbed me, Don. That's what I think. He robbed me – of being a kiddie, of having my own life without him in my head all the time. Of being normal. He robbed me of my family, of being able to have friends or get married to someone and have my own kids – he even robbed me of my true name. In a funny way, that's what gets to me most, because it's like, he robbed me of *myself*, and now – I don't know who I am …

We Came Down Off the Mountain

We came down off the mountain, and a warm wet time we had
    of it;
hours trudging through the red mud – the silence of the green
broken only by the rain falling and the sound of our passing.

The trees laced solid above us like the roof of a house
no one was living in; we climbed like thieves and descended
through the gullies all alone and fearful of the emptiness.

When we came to the place where the river ford should have
    been
it was all washed out, and the high, leaping brown water
raged and smashed the stones together with a noise like teeth
    grinding.

You found a stick and waded in like Moses leading some
lost tribe to Canaan; like a prophet, certain and mad.
I held your hand as the flood rose to my waist.

You smiled all the way across and I knew then
you had no fear of dying; but all I could think was,
it ends like this, in small mistakes and the fury of water.

Settler

When he said he'd got the offer of a really good job Out There
and they could emigrate directly after the wedding,
something had jumped in her guts; she wasn't sure *how* she felt …
But she saw the excitement in his eyes – somehow it seemed to
      catch hold of her;
and really, what was there to hold her in this *dump* of a town?
It was *so* beautiful Out There,
the photos in the brochures were like a gate into another world.

He loved it straightaway, fitted right in – loved the dense, silent
      land,
the folded hills so green and thick with trees they looked velvety.
He made friends easily with the careless
unconcern of a young man, ignoring what he couldn't change.
She tried, she *did* try – but it was hopeless.
She couldn't get a job, some immigration thing,
and she couldn't make friends with the women, they were so
      homey,
always trying to give her recipes for baking,
and cuttings for the tangled garden they called a 'section'.
She just couldn't imagine *them* going to a club, or wearing pretty
      clothes;
they talked about *books* – God! And other stuff that bored her silly.
She screamed when possums scrabbled on the tin roof at night,
and the strong, secret faces of the Maoris frightened her.
Everything in the shops was similar to home, but not the *same*;
The tea tasted strange and the chocolate was just *horrible*.
She cried, but he said she'd get used to it all, just give it time.

Outside, the crystal brilliance of the heated sky was veiled
with long white clouds drifting across its sapphire face;
the wind came off the sea, laden with salt and the scent of hibiscus.
Palm fronds clattered softly and there was snow on the distant
      mountains.
She looked out of the window and hated it so much she felt sick.
She hated the beauty, the wild stretches of empty land,
the yellow eye of the sun staring at her, judging her …

She put her sweater on and her teddy-bear slippers,
pulled all the curtains, locked the doors and put the TV on full
volume.
Then she lay on the sofa and sobbed loudly until she couldn't
breathe.

When he came home that night, she told him they were going
Home.
That was that, take it or leave it.
She couldn't stick it here and she bloody well *wouldn't*.
And this time, she took very great care not to look into his eyes …

Corazon

There is a fire burning on the hillside –
the smoke, a gauze-pale drifting ghost of the flames
rising against the long drop of the cliffs behind
like a memory of battles fought and forgotten.

The smell of wild thyme; of rosemary
and the ochre dust of the red earth desert ...

In the old house, cool and shadowed, only the
thick white walls are warmed by the savage light outside;
in the rooms, walk barefoot on terracotta tiles
stratified and crumbling with the wear of years.

The smell of eucalyptus branches burning in the
stone hearth; night jasmine; the velvet silence ...

In her niche by the door, the plaster Virgin
cradles El Niño; his robe rose-pink, her gown the blue
of the midday sky, the folds all patterned with gold;
her gleaming crown is heavy, the Queen of Heaven bows under its
      weight.

The scent of bitter oranges; of trees; of the flinty well-water;
of sweet vanilla cakes and red, oaky wine; of sleep ...

Of sleep in the silent fortress-house; the ancient stone
strong with the procession of generations,
stepping like a long, sun-filled dream through
summers and autumns, winters and springs.

Each morning, the great herds of goats pour down the valley,
sounding like a river of bells.
And like the animals, we move towards the light;
like the animals we are – through the seasons, to the light.

Brazil

In the taxi, do you remember? As we drove through
the vast wet heat of the tropic night, the burnt sugar smell
of the cane alcohol fuel and the reek of decay, simmering, alive...
No air, not a breath even from the taxi's movement.
I turned to look at you and close to your cheek, hovering,
was a huge night moth, the size of my two hands, greenish moon-
      pale,
its dark coiled tongue sucking up the tears and sweat from your
      skin.

I dream of it sometimes; I dream of Brazil.
I dream of the processions of little children
all dressed in white for the Virgin or some other, older goddess.
I hear their beating drums echoing through
the half-flooded village streets all night.
I dream of faces, ebony black with turquoise eyes,
or butter-yellow ringlets spilling over coffee-coloured shoulders.
I dream of the soft, unformed bodies of the diseased little
      prostitutes,
their rosy mouths embroidered with sores;
the great statue of Christ embracing nothing high above them all.

I see the shining, alabaster towers of the rich rising directly
out of the congealed slums – treasure on earth and death in rags
all heaped together under the Southern Cross.
I see men who fight like dancers, and raw-emerald waves crashing
onto the white sand that boils with thieves and tourists.
I see the street boys playing football like princes;
the straight-backed girls with their naked dignity.
I see the night children, all murdered now in the Cathedral square,
blood everywhere – blood, thick, rich coppery and sacred,
washing into the gutters, leaving no trace.

Don't ask me to make judgements. I dream often of justice and
      salvation,
I dream of fires burning on the beach and the stutter of guns;
but I never dream of answers, I never dream of answers anymore.

Gun

It's very easy to get a gun if you know the right people,
or at least people who know people – you let it be known
what you want and eventually you'll get the word.
That's it. That's what he did and the gun,
smooth, heavy and easy, lay in his pocket waiting.
Because guns wait, they wait until *you* decide what to
do with them, they just wait – and that made him happy.
In fact, the whole thing – setting up the buy,
going to the guy's house, handing over the money –
made him feel better than he'd ever felt before,
and just knowing he had the gun made him feel ten-foot tall.
He went into the pub with it; showed the lads
(under the table, mind), the oily steel gleaming in the half-light,
and man, were they impressed – he was so proud.
As he walked home he got a fantastic buzz just
knowing he had this gun and all the people
who went past him – ignoring him, not seeing him –
didn't know just how close they were to somebody special.

It's very easy to kill someone. Murder them and
it won't even make the front page – you don't even get famous
for doing it. Not that he'd meant to – not at all.
It had been the last thing in his mind.
What he'd wanted, you see, was for her to take him seriously.
He thought – when she saw the gun – she'd realise
he was a man, not some fucking boy.
He saw it in his mind – her gasping in admiration,
telling him what a bad man he was – all big eyes and open legs.
But – she just – she – she said he was a wanker,
and he could just piss off, right, just piss off,
trying to frighten her with a sodding toy gun . . .
It was all *wrong* …
And the gun was waiting, fitting neat and sweet in his hand …

They don't tell you about the stink of blood and brains,
or the noise – so loud and ringing. They don't tell you
about all that on the records or in the films.
So he was sick, and then went outside into the fresh air
to wait – the gun still in his hand, waiting with him.

Don't Look Down

I have this really clear little memory of walking through the park at dawn with a couple of friends, on our way home from some terrible party. I would have been about sixteen years old and I seem to see myself walking through the low, white mist that wound through the trees and lay like a breath exhaled across the neat lawns. I see our silly fashionable clothes, I see us laughing and laughing at some joke, our smeared faces aching with happiness and cold.

But what I remember so well isn't the joke or the laughter, or even my friends, whose faces I can only make out dimly now, like they were floating under ice. I just remember feeling suddenly that anything was possible for me, that I could live forever, that I could make astonishing things happen if I just set my mind to it and hung on with all my strength no matter what. It felt like great wings beating, beating through the storm of fear inside of me, all mixed up with the laughter and the cold – it was like a great bird set free and flying into the light.

And now, you know, I don't see too well. That savage light blinded me, those wings carried me along so fast it took my breath away and all I thought was, *don't look down, never look down – then you won't see the danger and you won't be afraid.*

People thought I was brave, I let them think that – but I wasn't. I just never looked down.

Love

I remember hearing this woman screaming in our alley once. I listened, along with half the terrace, I suppose, as she raged on – begging, threatening, crying for her ex-boyfriend to open his door and talk to her. It was funny, but it wasn't – you know – being too close to the bone for comedy. Saying that, mind, no doubt the lad would try to make it a laugh in the pub that night ...

Yellin' her fuckin' head off she were, silly bitch ... let her in? Did I fuck! I'm not daft, I'm well out of it, I can tell yer – stupid cow! He laughs uncomfortably, shifting in his seat, taking a pull of his beer. *Women! Fuckin' hell, man, I ask yer! More trouble than they're fuckin' worth, eh?* and he hopes to God she doesn't go to the Club that night and show him up in front of his mates.

She'd just stood there in the icy wind, blown bits of rubbish snagging round her thin white ankles; shouting and shouting, getting more tired and more desperate, a raw whining edge creeping into her voice.

Sean, Sean, how can you trait me like this? It's not fair, you've got to talk to me – Sean, open the door, I know you're in there – Sean, please – how can I mean nowt to yer after three years – three years! I love yer, I love yer – let me in and talk to yer – God, Sean, how can yer be such a bastard – how can yer? What have I done? What have I ever done wrong to yer?

Eventually, after half an hour or so, she and the silent friend she had brought with her as a witness trailed off, her sobs fading as she tottered off down the setts on her rickety platform shoes. The terrace returned to silence. I shut the front door and put the kettle on.

Christ, it even hurts at second-hand, doesn't it?

Corky and His Life

Corky cycling into town on a catalogue mountain bike,
no helmet, cheap trainers and his rubbery beer gut bouncing;
just a bloke doing some last-minute keep-fit.
No one special, nice enough, just himself – wheezing round the corner
as the boy in the sporty little GTI pulls out without looking, like they
      do.
Something going out, something coming in …

There's a slowness to accidents – like honey oozing off the spoon,
and in a kind of flight Corky hits the curb with his head, bang on.
A spider's web of fractures laces his skull, his thick brown curls
matted with blood, while the boy chatters platitudes in panic
and Corky sprawls with his brain juddering in its bony shell
and something going out, something coming in …

Two years later and Corky walks a bit – not far, in case he forgets the
way home to his missus, who cries because she wants Corky back
like he was before – not this moody, jelly-eyed stranger who pushes
Corky's limbs around and answers to his name; who hauls the carcass
of its host to doctors, hospitals and clinics none of whom knew Corky
before something went out, and something came in …

John Corcoran's not dead but Corky is. There's worse ways of being
than the ones you look away from – like the wheelchair, the scars,
the leg off at the knee. You could be dead inside your own head.
You could lose everything that matters like lovers, friends and family
because whatever it is that makes you yourself, gets pulped and
      mashed
by some witless twat in a car he can't control on a road he doesn't
      know.

And whatever you were goes out with your breath like a blown match,
and the thing that creeps into that emptiness
is old and cold – and its name is Death-in-Life.

Stranger

When I first got married, I went to live in a cold,
narrow flat in a cold, narrow little hilltop village crouched on the
     edge
of the moor – a village that crawled craven under the iron shadow
of the old Moravian Church and did not welcome outsiders.
I was alone a lot, because my husband worked away.
I had no close friends, and I was a stranger to my family and his.
So, eventually, isolation laid its cold curse on my heart and I
     began to
go quietly insane in that crooked, windswept place.

It's very hard to explain now, with the cats playing round
my feet and this nice, bright house full of voices,
the dreadful terror and despair that dropped like a fall of poisoned
water through my guts each night and made my heart beat too loud,
     too fast.
How the dark things – dark and dazzling as when you look
too long into the sun – surfaced grimacing and cackling
from where I thought I had buried them forever in my
     not-remembering.

On one of those midnights I looked at the
old kitchen knife with a kind of desperate relief.
The raggedy rip and saw seemed a merciful ending to a worthless
     life,
and with a terrible clarity I knew I could do it
and there was no one to stop me but myself.
So I grabbed the phone and dialed at random –
the numbers flying out like a mathematical prayer
and someone answered, a man answered …

and lost and mad as I was, he didn't turn me away.
He listened and talked for nearly an hour
and when I felt tired, I put the phone down.
I never asked his name, he never asked mine;
and I remember saying goodbye,
but I don't remember thanking him for saving my life.

Mermaids

I want to go swimming every day, sliding beneath the
chemical water – gliding like a seal towards the deep end.
I want to swim forever, on and on and on and on,
blinkered by goggles, entranced by the circular rhythms of
    breathing
and pulling, pulling through the amniotic pool.

I want to go swimming every day, for hours and hours,
until I find a way to eel out of the city and into the breathing Deeps;
into the vast Unknowable; rolling with the surf,
floating in the world ocean – pacific, beatific,
fearless into the blue dissolving.

Mother of Oceans, Queen of the Seas – bless us all;
lovers of the great salt water and mermaids of the chlorine sea.

The Blue Car

The police car pulled up a little ahead and the officer got out and walked slowly toward him, not wishing to frighten him. They'd met before, several times – everybody at the station knew Dickie.

'Now then, Dickie boy, what's all this? What you been up to, lad? Someone's complained about you – now, have you been taking your tablets like you should, eh?'

Dickie turned his red, crumpled face towards the voice he heard. He felt the image of the thing he'd done surge back to him like a salt wave – it was about his car, his blue car, he knew it. It *was* his. He'd only gone to touch it, make sure it was solid, real, when the woman had come out of the house sharp as a knife, the sun sparking off her big earrings and the diamond stud in her nose. She had snapped at him, the hardness of the words hurting him, dinning in his ears like the clash of metal – so he had to shout a bit to make her hear him, make her give him back his beautiful blue car. She had looked at him slitty-eyed like a cat, maybe even *hissed*, and stepped back into the darkness. Dickie's head buzzed with the memory. The sun was very hot, it made everything difficult to see, but he knew the policeman, remembered him – or was it another one? Weren't they all the same person? Just more of The Others, The Controllers. Dickie knew all about Them, that's why They were always getting at him and Mum.

'My car, she had my blue car – that woman – my car, the one Mum got me, you remember, you should, you're a *policeman*, Mum says I've to do as you say …'

His voice rose to a see-sawing screech. The officer radioed the station telling them to phone the hospital. He was bringing them Richard Lawrence again.

The stifling stink of the hospital made Dickie sneeze, so he sneezed as much as possible because it helped prevent the contamination, and he sang his interference tune as best he could, while a lady doctor asked him things about his car, and why he had shouted. He wanted to answer her, but he knew if he stopped singing he'd die of the poisonous gas that accumulated in buildings – so he breathed as little as he could and kept up his mantra. He would have happily written down the answers to their questions, but no one suggested that, and Dickie didn't think it his place to just grab a pen and write. They didn't like sudden movement in places like this, he knew that much.

He began to worry about Mum, out there with no one to protect her from The Others, and he felt a great pressure of fear build up in his guts. Tears burnt through his eyes, which he knew was a sign of the poison getting to him, so he tried to run away, back to Mum – but a big nurse man called Phil and the doctor and the policeman grabbed him. When he was still again, he felt wet and uncomfortable and he was ashamed and cried more.

The doctor sighed. 'Phil, take Mr Lawrence to Ward 6 and clean him up, I'll be along shortly. What, Officer? Oh, yes, it's a side effect of the medication – loss of bladder control, dribbling, that sort of thing … Anyway, fine, I'll contact his mother. Pardon? A bit of a lost soul? Yes, yes, you could say that – well, goodbye.'

She shuffled through Dickie's file and dialled the number. After a while she spoke. 'Mrs Lawrence? It's Doctor Jones at St Peter's. Yes, it's Dickie – no, he's OK, but … Yes, it's the car thing again – has he been taking his … Oh, well, never mind, we'll get him straight again, but he *must* try to be regular with the tablets … Well, yes, I realise it's hard to keep him inside under the circumstances, but … Yes, yes, he *is* a grown lad now, I know, but … He's only twenty-three, Mrs Lawrence, there's always hope, there's new research going on all the time and … Yes, yes, I'm sorry, I realise it's just the two of you, I'm sorry – I … Mrs Lawrence? *Mrs Lawrence?* Oh *God*.'

Putting down the phone, she pleated the stiff material of her white coat between her fingers, and stared at the tottering mass of papers on her desk. If she listened hard, she could hear Dickie howling his prayer. It was 'Singin' in the Rain'.

I'm sin-gin' in the rain, just sin-gin' in the rain, what-a glor-rious fee-ling, I-I'm ha-ppy a-gain ...

'You keep on singing, Dickie boy, just you keep on singing,' she thought. 'God knows we need all the help we can get.'

Nativity

It was one of those crumbling old houses round by the University that were built for wealthy Victorian businessmen, but are now carved into warrens of student flats and horrible bedsitters. Knocking on the door made a damp, rotten noise and the smell of old garbage was vile. I didn't expect to find him. Having searched all evening and turned up no trace I had given up hope – only duty kept me going. Not that he was blood family or even a friend really, just a hopeless little wannabe punk with the wrong clothes and that sort of pasty, unformed face that always annoys drunks. His name was Darren. He was fifteen. He had been abandoned by his family like a Christmas puppy and had adopted me in his drifting, gormless way a few months previously. I felt sorry for him. Boys like that don't have mates, they're too uncool, too much of a social liability. There wasn't anyone to bother about him when he went missing – so I felt obliged, somehow, to look for him.

I knocked again and this time a fat, panda-eyed punkette let me in. It was 1981 and punk was *not* dead in the Northlands. I could hear the Ruts on someone's croaky stereo and there was a Clash poster on the door my hostess said was Darren's. The place reeked of damp, dope and Jasmine joss-sticks. I couldn't wait to leave. I'd just see he was OK, then I'd go. I rapped on the peeling door. Faintly, I heard his voice asking who it was. He sounded terrible – stoned, weak.

I went in. He was sprawled in an old armchair, his yellow eyes rolling, a bottle of cider and one of cough syrup on the floor at his feet – the Poor Boys' Cocktail. He said hello with a dazed smile. I asked him what he thought he was up to, vanishing like that, worrying people. I realised I sounded like my mother. I shut up awkwardly, wondering what to do, when he gestured to the corner of the room.

'I bin lookin' after Reena – ma girlfrien' – thass Reena …'

On a filthy, burst mattress on the floor lay a skinny girl of about thirteen, sleeping twitchily. Her enormous pregnant belly was in unnatural contrast to her soft little arms and childlike face. She breathed heavily through her mouth. Her dirty hands plucked at the old, unzipped sleeping bag that covered her. Around her lips were splatters of sores. Crumpled crisp packets still leaking glue lay beside her.

'Not my babby,' Darren said in the earnest, mushy voice of the totally smashed. 'Her Dad's babby. But me, I'll tek care on 'em, mek a fammly. Like you allus sayin', mmm. You know, tek – tek res-pon-sib-il-ity. Mek ma own fammly. Like you said, na? Ah – I'm – I'm goin' ter *do the right thing*, yeah.'

Darren smiled again, his hazy features lit with heroism. I remembered all the times I'd expounded my great social theories in the cheap nightclub we all went to, never realising Darren was treating every word as gospel. I didn't know what to say to him. All my bravado leaked away with the tears that tracked down my face. There was nothing I could do. Darren nodded off and I stuffed some money in his pocket and left.

After a couple of days, I went back with a handful of leaflets and some grand idea of rescue. I was too late. The fat punkette said they'd gone off to London owing the rent. I threw the leaflets in the bin.

That's it. I don't know what happened to them. I wish I did, but things don't work that way. Darren and Reena. No room at the bloody Inn. No Guiding Star. No Three Wise Men. No hay-warm Stable. No Away in a Manger. Just the Little Madonna of the Glue Bag and her Boy Joseph. And the Christ Child in her belly crucified before he was born.

Dining With Duke Humphrey

Colin sits waiting his turn at the Blood Donor Centre, rehearsing in his mind what he wants to say. He knows it's a bad habit, making his eventual speech sound forced and unnatural, but he's afraid he'll get mixed up – so he silently goes over and over his question. He doesn't realise his lips are moving. He doesn't realise that his cardigan is inside out and his socks don't match. Eventually, hearing his name called, he folds his mac over his arm and goes to the woman at the desk.

'I have a question.' He states this much louder than he intended.

The woman looks up, startled, and seeing Colin in his cardigan, his wonky black-framed glasses and thin, white face, her expression changes to repressed irritation. Colin doesn't notice – the words he so carefully prepared are coming out of his mouth in a torrent.

'I – I want to know, you see, I want to know if you're selling this blood – our blood, the blood we're giving – I – you see – I want to know if you're selling it to private hospitals. I'm against that, you understand, very much against it – yes. I read only recently in the newspaper, *The Guardian*, not a tabloid – I don't read them; but I read that the Health Minister said …'

'I'll get Doctor for you, Mr er – Hawkins, she'll be able to answer you properly. If you'll just sit back in the waiting area …'

Colin's mouth shuts with an audible snap. As he refolds his mac, he hears a splatter of giggles behind him and a boy's low, jeering voice imitating him.

'*Not a tab-loid, ho no, Hi don't read them* … looney fucker – what's he fucking on about? Twats like him want putting away, honest.'

'Shut *up*, Dave, he might hear yer, poor thing. Look at state of him, he's not right – Dave, *Dave*, give *up* now …' The girl giggles again behind her hand.

Colin sits down quickly. Under the bunched up mac his hands twist, the bony knuckles cracking, and he pauses their motion only to push his glasses back up his beaky nose. He realises vaguely how people see him. He's not stupid. It's just that other things, important things, seem to matter more than clothes and food and what silly girls think. His head is a continuous whirl of articles he's read, programmes he's heard on Radio Four. He doesn't have a TV. Father hated them and, after he died, Mother still didn't like to go against his wishes and get one. It would have seemed a betrayal of Father's principles, in some way. They would sit there, in the evenings, Mum knitting and Colin reading, the radio still tuned to Father's choice of channel.

Colin hears more stifled laughter and insults. He feels that terrible urge to cry welling up in him again, making him blink and swallow. He wishes Mum hadn't passed away too. He wishes he could be in the sitting room again in the snug warmth of the gas fire, hearing the soothing repetitive click of Mum's needles and her breathy sighs. He wishes he could get things straight – could get across to people how he feels about what's right and wrong, politics, books, ideas. Could live up to Dad. He looks at his cardigan and realises despairingly it's inside out. *Can't I do anything right?* The world narrows sharply, painfully, back to the ugly room and the exasperated voice of a woman saying, 'Mr Hawkins, *Mr Hawkins* … Doctor will see you now – this way, please.'

He gets up and follows, past the gigglers, past the people who'd rather not look at him. *Now I'll get an answer*, he thinks. It's important to know what's going on behind our backs. I don't want my blood sold off to anyone just because they're rich, it should be fair shares for all like Dad always said. I want to know what's going on. I have a right to know.

And scruffily, hungrily, his hair stuck up at all angles and the world forgotten, he marches into the doctor's office.

Wuthering Heights

Her parents named her Emily, because they'd just moved up North so that her father could take up the post of Headmaster at Shaw Grange Comprehensive. They were so close to Haworth that naming her after one of the famous Brontës seemed a sort of good omen. Not that, to be honest, either of her parents had actually read *Wuthering Heights* – those Victorian romances always seemed so hysterical – but the name 'Emily' had a sweet, old-fashioned ring to it. Her father thought it 'sounded like a real *daughter's* name'. They always had a good laugh together about that, it was quite the family joke.

Emily, though obviously a very bright child, unhappily wasn't a pretty one. She inherited her father's squarish head and protuberant eyes – the eyes that earned him the schoolyard nickname of 'Owd Popeye'. She also had her mother's sallow, uneven complexion and thin, hesitantly curling black hair. She was wiry and short as well – 'no figure at all, none – may as well be a *boy,*' her Nana used to comment every Christmas. They were not happy occasions, those family get-togethers. But Emily did extremely well at school, really excelled, and was absolutely no trouble whatsoever at home. Consequently, when she expressed the desire to learn how to ice-skate – after she'd seen it on TV – her parents were happy to let her. Provided, naturally, it didn't interfere with homework.

Emily loved it – she *loved* it; so much so that she barely mentioned it at home. Skating was her secret passion, it belonged to her alone, it sang in her heart like a wild bird. And she was good at it – very good – as good as she was at school; but oh, what a difference, what a gulf, what a *galaxy* of difference between being good at Maths and Physics, and the pure, inexpressible physical joy of whirling round the ice looping and flying like a little kestrel. It was effortless, swooping across the gleaming, scored, blue-white ice to the tinny magic of the latest hits on tape over the loudspeakers. She had lessons and then a coach. Her coach thought he'd found a winner; she had *it*, that perfect ease, pure talent. She was a plain little piece and no mistake – which didn't go down well with the judges usually – but with a red spangly costume and some clever make-up, who'd notice in the face of that ability, that *at-homeness* on the ice. She went in for local competitions and won. She went in for national competitions and won. She brought her trophies home with careful nonchalance, showed them briefly to her parents, who were polite about it and said the right things, and then hid them in her wardrobe. Equally carefully, she made sure she passed all her exams with excellent grades. At the school's excited request she applied to Oxford and got in easily. She talked long and hard with her coach at practice sessions while other young hopefuls tottered about unsteadily and battered the ice with blunt skates.

Then she went home and told her parents she wanted to be a professional ice-dancer, not go to university, not go to Oxford. She begged, she begged quietly, her voice low and her eyes fixed on the old-gold fitted carpet; she pleaded for her life in the face of her parents' utter astonishment and incomprehension. She fetched her trophies and her certificates, even the clippings from the local newspaper. Tears fell from her soft brown popeyes as her father, enraged, phoned her coach and told him in no uncertain terms never to speak to Emily again – shouting red-faced into the receiver – what had the fool been thinking of, filling the girl's head with ridiculous nonsense. He rounded on Emily nearly screaming – she was going to Oxford, *Oxford*, my God, she was *not* going to throw away everything they'd worked for. *He* may not have had the chance of Oxford, but his daughter *would* and that was that. Skating? *Skating* – for Christ's sake it was a hobby, a *hobby*, not real life. There were ice rinks in Oxford, she could still go at weekends, let that be an end to it, and no more of this hysterical behaviour. Her mother cried too, but not like Emily cried all that night as the wind howled off the moor and shook the double-glazing.

When I knew Emily, she was finishing a PhD at Leeds – something scientific. She had a room in the run-down shared house in Bradford where I was living. Every Saturday morning she went to Silver Blades in leggings and a sweatshirt, and came home with wild red roses brightening her sallow cheeks. One night, when we were both up late, she told me she'd once had a beautiful skating dress, a costume in crimson with thousands of sequins, that her coach's wife had made for her. She said the little skirt went in a sparkling ripple like sun on water when she twirled on the tips of her white skates. I asked her if she'd been named after Emily Brontë and she said yes, she had. She said she'd read *Wuthering Heights*, often; she said she thought Emily Brontë would have enjoyed skating, in her opinion. Then, in her sensible beige candlewick dressing gown, she poured herself some tea and went back to her room to study.

The Wool Exchange, Bradford

Dusty darkness ribbed with beams arcing into space,
glittering motes dancing in light skewering from high, dirty
      windows
and the great roof – like an upturned boat; like a mediaeval casket,
steepling to angels, their gold peeling, their praying hands clotted
with neglect.

Every great pillar is carved with a different plant,
the stone made vegetal by men consumed with their archaic honour,
their chisels turning the bones of earth into gardens
so other men in lost times could walk like princes
in a bower.

That it was built for trade doesn't matter; the raw chatter
of the wool barons dealing never pierced its secular cloisters.
It is not *their* monument, but the grace and sacrament
of the nameless men who put their souls into the making
of this place.

The Test

This is a story that forms part of a larger work in progress. This section concerns a time in my life – I was in my early twenties – when I was married to Kes, who became a member of the outlaw motorcycle gang 'Satan's Slaves'. It was first published – in a slightly different form – by the motorcycle magazine 'Backstreet Heroes'.

Occasionally, we would be obliged to go to one of the official parties. Sometimes these were held at one of the Slaves' homes. More worrying were the ones where we were invited to party with another gang on their territory. The houses where these exercises in mayhem took place always seemed to look the same though – big, dirty old Victorian places, with backyards full of discarded machinery and the carcasses of dead bikes and cars.

They were always cold, damp places too – except for the front room where a gas fire with broken ceramic elements would be hissing on full blast and glowing a furnace orange. I'm sure half the feeling of being horribly stoned was actually carbon monoxide poisoning. On this particular night, the house belonged to a Biker Legend – a man so terrifying that even hardened old bikers spoke of him in a tone of marked respect. He was extremely handsome, very Clint Eastwood, and had his own gang that operated from a small village on the moors near Morecambe. The only noticeable difference between the Legend's house and any of the others we partied in was the huge incongruous fire surround in the front room. It was carved from white marble – now much stained and battered – and above it was an ornate, tarnished mirror framed in rococo gold. They were obviously relics of the house's former days of glory. Now the mirror reflected the chaos of a gang party, the discoloured silver lending a curious, hellish distortion to the images it contained.

I never enjoyed these parties. They reminded me of the dinner parties my parents held for my father's bosses and the bosses' lacquered wives. I'd hated those evenings of being on my best behaviour *or else*, and these parties – despite the outlaw trappings – made me feel the same. I knew one false move, one word out of turn and I'd let Kes down, just as I knew I'd let my parents down. What Kes felt about it I don't know, as he was never one for unnecessary talking.

But what could I do? I could hardly turn round to him and say, *take me home, I don't like it, I'm not up to it, I'm scared*. We'd done so well on the Run – not too fast, not too slow – no stops other than the mass ones, no breakdowns. Nothing, in fact, that would draw attention to us or lump us in with the laggards and the losers. No, I couldn't back out, not after the months and months of careful manoeuvring and the exquisitely timed political game-playing. No corporate wife ever worked as hard as I did, believe me – and for what? The dream of family, of honour bright, of one-for-all and all-for-one? I think I believed in the brilliant, savage dream of it more than those men ever did. Hadn't I read all the books, seen all the films? The reality, however, was another, brutal matter. They were men. They got the Patch, the rig, the glory. I was a woman and I got the hierarchy of matrons, the brood mares savagely mindful of their position and status in the tribe. Straighter, under their biker-chick chic, than any member of the society they affected to despise, and more narrow minded than a Virginia Evangelical.

But here we were, and it wouldn't do to be caught *thinking*. Already Big Pam was bridling in my direction, her lardy face writhing with suspicion. To make me sweat she whispered an aside to her cohort, Mand. They sniggered and felt in their hand-tooled leather handbags for a smoke, eyes glistening with malice. I felt sick with fatigue and tension. Careless of etiquette I sat next to Doc on a sagging sofa that reeked of cat piss, his crumpled gnome's face lazy with drink and cheerful cynicism. I hoped he'd protect me while Kes went off to inspect some marvel of engineering in the yard.

'Want some acid? Plenty acid round 'ere – blotter, mind you – wouldn't care for it meself, like, it's cut wi' strych. Fuckin' hard on the guts in my opinion, but there you are, youth of today, fucked, the lot on 'em.' He gestured at a cadaverously thin boy dressed in skintight greasy black leather, giggling through rotting green teeth at nothing *I* could see. 'Fucked in the head, eh, bolloxed – silly cunt. Still, if yer want some …'

'Yeah, see what you mean – no, I don't like it anymore meself, actually.'

'Don't yer, *actually* – ho, pard-on *me*, milady,' he said in a 'posh' voice. I froze – was he in a bad mood after all? Was he on a paranoia speed thing like last week? He was smiling, but that didn't necessarily mean he was OK. I must have looked like a frightened rabbit because he laughed and passed me his beer: 'Get yer gob round that, guaranteed blotter-free, the only fuckin' one in 'ere, believe me.'

I drank the warm, sweet-sour fluid and tried to relax as I gazed around the room, being careful not to linger too long on one person. I didn't want anyone to think I was dead-eyeing them. There were Outlaws from all over the country, plus hangers-on of all varieties. A couple of baby Grebos had sneaked in and were fucked on free acid. One of them had tried to pet our host's German Shepherd and it had bitten clean through his upper lip which was hanging half on, half off in a swollen, blackened mess. *He* thought it was some sort of badge of courage and kept repeating the story at the top of his voice. There were some older, mean-looking guys in one corner, with sharp, pallid prison faces and concealed guns that everyone knew about but elaborately ignored. And there were unattached women, too – some confident, long-time party girls hoping to score a steady fella and a boost up the social ladder – some pitiful, drunken losers with 'victim' written in block capitals on their raddled, cacky foreheads. And there was also Nidge's Fuck-of-the-Month, a middle-class art student unaware that Nidge was so riddled with the clap his dick-end looked like a leper's fist. She was thrilled with her bit of rough and her slumming expedition and her voice cut like a buzz saw.

She was me, I thought, me. Except I'd married my working-class hero and she was just wearing hers like a brooch. But unlike me, I thought smugly, she was stupid – and drunker than was safe. Inch by unsaveable inch I watched with horrible fascination as she crept closer and closer towards disaster. Then it happened – in the blink of an eye.

'Nidge, Nidge, don't be such a *wanker*, give me a fucking *drink* …'

Her voice sliced through the noise cleanly and fatally as she took the whisky bottle from Nidge's lips in front of us all. Without a second's hesitation, Nidge punched her in the face with the economical action of a man used to winning. Her high-bridged nose broke with an audible crack and a red blossom of blood. Her world fell apart like a badly stitched frock. Nidge turned away while she stumbled, sobbing from the room and out of the house. He was done with her, and he didn't give a fuck. I looked away – it was bad luck to see these things.

Then, suddenly, the Legend himself was sitting companionably on the arm of the sofa, talking to Doc. I tried not to stare. He was a major celebrity, famed for exploits such as biting a bloke's nose off in a fight *and swallowing it*. Tasted of blood, snot and gristle, he'd say cheerily. He rode a dragon-green rig with impressive artwork on the tank, and in every way behaved like a Star. Doc made careful compliments about the party and the beautiful rig, which was parked in the kitchen, while I tried to look keen, yet cool. I must have succeeded because the Legend addressed me personally, a thing normally unknown in the social annals of Outlaw Bikerdom.

'I ent seen yer before, who's yer Old Man?' he enquired affably.

I froze with terror. Doc answered for me, as was the custom, that my Old Man was their Prospect. I nodded, mute. The Legend nodded, too. He was very, very handsome, and through the horrible fear a vista of lust and social advancement opened up only to immediately fade at the knowledge of his rock-hard wife and two little blond sons. When I wakened from this foolish reverie, I realised not being on the ball had been a very bad mistake. The Legend was smiling in a wolfish sort of way and Doc looked worried. Something was amusing the Great Man. He spoke.

'Doc 'ere says you're a bit posh, like. Eh? Eh? Tell yer what, you come wi' me, an I'll show yer summat a bit *posh* …'

He uncoiled himself from the sofa arm and weaved through the party with me in his wake. I had no choice but to follow him after a direct request. The noise quietened and all eyes followed our progress, the men grinning and their women nudging each other. It was like a bad dream from which I could not escape, and all I could do was tell myself not to panic or I was done for. We neared the ruined mantelshelf and our dank, distorted reflections wavered in the flyblown mirror as if it were a dirty pond. The atmosphere was thick and hot with expectation. The Legend gestured languidly to a large domed birdcage draped in a cloth on the mantelshelf. I heard Doc whisper 'oh shit' but I felt a wave of relief. A birdcage – wow – it was obviously some sort of exotic bird, a big old parrot or something – I mean, a *birdcage*, well …

The Legend swept off the cover.

'That posh enough for yer, eh?'

It was not, after all, a birdcage. It was a very large, thick-glass jar. In it, immersed in a murky fluid, was a severed head. Its eyes were half-shut, its mouth – a soft, small mouth – partly open. Long hair floated around it like weed. It was the head of a young girl. I heard the men's laughter echo in the white, sweaty coldness that enveloped me and I heard, as if from very far away, the Legend proudly boasting he got her off a bent mortician for over a hundred quid. Then a woman started screaming shrilly 'god, god, god' over and over and the Legend grumpily covered up his prize. With careful deportment, I walked to the stinking toilet and threw up in private.

It had been a test. I had passed. Doc was pleased with me and I didn't shame my Old Man. So that was OK. That was OK – wasn't it?

Anger and Fear

Anger makes you do the things you do,
it moves your mouth to speak as you do,
it runs like thin wires of electricity through
your limbs, branding you with its heat.

Anger and fear are Siamese twins
bound together by unholy flesh,
but don't be afraid – you aren't the only one.

I know they told you that you were alone,
I know that's what makes you so afraid.
They controlled you that way
when you were small and lonely.

Fear and anger feed off each other
like cannibal crows tearing each other to bits,
but don't be afraid – you aren't the only one.

I am not afraid of your anger because
however angry you are, you aren't as angry as me.
And anyway, it's not your fault –
it just hurts me to see you suffer.

Anger and fear dance a strange waltz,
round and round they go to music we cannot hear;
but don't be afraid – you aren't the only one.

He Said

He said, 'What do you want for Christmas?'

And she couldn't think of anything.

(Only, little white lights wound through pine branches,
satsumas and cloves – fruitcake oozing vanilla and raisins –
golden chocolate coins and small plastic toys that break
*   straightaway.*
Snow mittens on elastic and red wellingtons.
A bicycle – a wad of book tokens, a big panda teddy,
a fire in the hearth and the first safe warmth of sleep ...)

'I don't want anything,' she said – and then quickly
because she didn't want to hurt his feelings,
'I mean, there must be something, but I can't think,
you choose, you choose me something – a surprise.'

(Only, just not Nana tipsy on G&T's singing the Welsh
National Anthem in Welsh and mourning for the long lost,
*   deep-sided*
valley echoing with the family she abandoned to improve herself.
Just not Mum and Dad, drunk since morning,
scraping and scraping at the brute archaeology of old wounds.
Just not herself as a child, frantically trying to build a Christmas
out of things she'd read in books and seen on
the Sunday Classic teatime series on the telly;
Dickens, the Brontës, actors in costume
with red cheeks and stories that always turned out well.
No, not herself, building in her heart a shiny fragile wall of tinsel,
wrapping paper, baubles and stars to hide behind,
while the muttering battles sniped and grated round her –
and – and – 'it's all my fault – it's all my fault – it's all my fault'
dinning in her feverish head until she vomited up her dinner
and was sent to bed in disgrace.)

'But you must want something,' he said, puzzled;
'bath stuff or clothes, or some books – you like books – or …'

'You choose,' she said, 'you choose something for me, love.'

And he held her against his chest while she cried and cried
and couldn't stop, or breathe, or tell him why.

Redemption

We will have redemption, we will be redeemed;
no terror in the night can bind us and no bitterness destroy.
The future will be moon-clear and the past will be our guide;
as sorrow waters new growth, so pain will make us strong.
We will have redemption, we will be redeemed.
By the chaos of the sea and the black earth in our hands,
by the surge of breath that drives us and our own imperfect lives,
by the pure curve of a child's face and the mottled hand of age,
by animals, by faith, by kindness and by blood.
We will have redemption, we will be redeemed.

All of us – the lost, the broken and the fearful;
those of us still searching and those of us still dreaming,
those of us who live as outlaws and those of us tormented.
The gentle and the simple, the cynical and the savage,
we will have redemption, we will be redeemed.
With our own hands we will make it,
with our own lips we will seal it,
in our own hearts we will keep it, sweet and true.
This by my own promise – I swear it will be so,
we will have redemption, we will be redeemed.